MACHINES

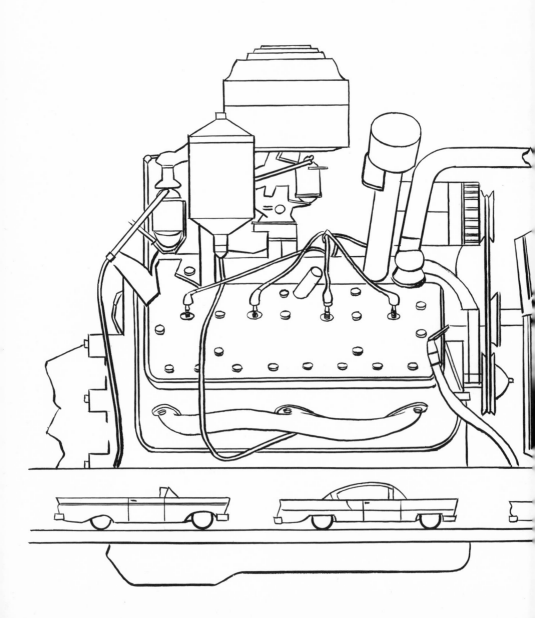

how things work:

machines

jerome s. meyer

illustrated by john polgreen

WORLD PUBLISHING
TIMES MIRROR
NEW YORK

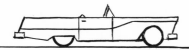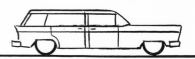

TO

Ferris Werbin

Published by The World Publishing Company
Published simultaneously in Canada
by Nelson, Foster & Scott Ltd.

1972 Printing

Library of Congress catalog card number: 58-9420
ISBN 0-529-04576-1 (Trade edition)
ISBN 0-529-04578-8 (Library edition)
Printed in the United States of America

WORLD PUBLISHING
TIMES MIRROR

Contents

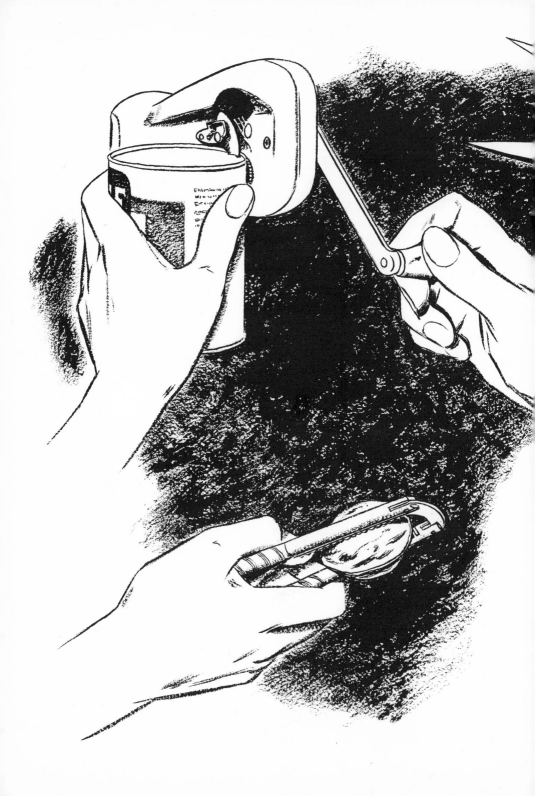

A MACHINE is any man-made device with movable parts that does work for us. Even the simplest machines save us a great deal of time and effort.

Try to crack a walnut with your fingers. You simply can't do it. Now put the walnut in a nutcracker and press the arms of the nutcracker together. The nut cracks instantly with only a little effort on your part. A nutcracker is a very simple machine.

Try to open a can of food without a can opener. You can't do it. A can opener is another very simple machine. In the same sense, a pair of scissors is a machine and so is any other tool with movable parts that does work for us.

None of these machines will work by themselves, however. The power, or force, to make the parts move must come from outside the machine. A nutcracker does work only when you use the power of your hand to move its arms. If you remove your hand, the nutcracker cannot work. It takes both you and the nutcracker to make a working machine.

In order to understand machines, it is important to understand what is meant by the word "work" in relation to machines. Of course, we all know what work is in everyday life. Most people work to earn a living. But in machines the word work means force, acting over a distance to overcome some resistance. A machine does work only when its

[8]

parts move, no matter how short a distance they move. If a man-made device does not have movable parts nor the necessary power to move its parts, it is not a machine.

You work exactly the way a machine works whenever you lift something heavy, walk upstairs, or use up energy to do something. Your physical strength or energy is the force, or power to produce motion, and your arms and legs are the movable parts.

But suppose you, using yourself as a machine, wanted to get up to a platform 50 feet in the air. Obviously, it would be absurd to try to jump that high. No one could do it, because no one has that much physical strength.

The only possible way to get up to that platform by yourself is to move in gradual stages or steps. In order to do this you must take your time. It might take twenty or thirty times longer for you to walk upstairs or climb a ladder than it would if you could reach the platform in one jump. And, of course, your legs—the movable parts of you as a machine—move back and forth as many more times as there are steps leading to the platform. In other words, they travel more distance. But by taking your time and moving a long distance in gradual steps you can do something that is impossible to do by yourself in any other way.

Machines do their work in the same way.

The work of machines is measured in units of force multiplied by distance.

This unit of work is called a foot-pound. If you lift one pound of something one foot, you are doing one foot-pound of work. If you weigh 70 pounds and walk upstairs a distance of 20 feet, you are doing 20 times 70 pounds or 1,400 foot-pounds of work.

In order to do that many foot-pounds of work you must do it gradually, but the interesting fact is that by using a little force over a long distance you can produce great force over a short distance.

A force of only 10 pounds moving a distance

of 100 feet can lift a weight of 1,000 pounds a distance of one foot, because 10 pounds times 100 feet equals 1,000 pounds times one foot. That is why a man using an automobile jack can lift a heavy car. By moving the handle of the jack up and down many times and taking a long time to do it, he can lift that heavy load. But he can lift it only a foot or two.

Except for a small amount of energy that is lost through friction of the moving parts rubbing together, the foot-pounds of work that a machine will produce always equal the work put into the machine. You can't get more out of a machine than you put into it. That is why perpetual motion is impossible.

So far, the only force that we have discussed has been the strength of one person. This was the only kind of power that primitive man used, and so the work he could do was very limited. Later, he learned to use animals and wind and water as sources of power. These gave him more strength to produce

motion. His machines could do more work, but none of these sources of power except water was very dependable. A man or an animal may get sick or lose strength; the wind dies down. No one can count on them to do the same amount of work every day.

There was another disadvantage to these sources of power: they were separate from the movable parts of the machine. A machine must have both motion and the power to produce motion in order to work. If the power stopped—if a man went home to eat his dinner, or an animal got sick, or the wind died—the work of the machine stopped, too.

The invention of the steam engine, the gas engine, and the electric motor changed all this. These machines gave us great power that could be counted on to do the same amount of work day in and day out. And for the first time, it was possible to put this power into the machine with the movable parts.

These two changes were so important that they revolutionized the work of the world. For as soon as man found a way to make his machines work steadily, doing the same amount of work every day, and could build

the power right into the machine, he became a giant who could do work that had been impossible to do before.

The slow, undependable horse and buggy that could travel only a few miles a day became the fast automobile, always ready to go and able to travel mile after mile, night and day. The slow, laborious work of human beings who worked long hours to produce our daily needs was taken over by factories filled with huge, complicated machines that could work around the clock. Tractors, combines, and trucks replaced draft animals on farms;

sailing ships gave way to fast steamships crossing the ocean every few days on regular schedules. The drudgery of pumping water by hand became a simple matter of turning on a water tap.

This revolution in power happened only about 200 years ago. We are still living in the Age of Power it created.

Power has made it possible for us to build machines of many different kinds. But the moving parts of all machines still operate on only four basic principles, which have been known since earliest times. These are the wheel and axle, the lever, the screw, and the wedge.

Primitive man knew these principles and used them. Simple machines powered by men or animals, or by wind and water, also used them. All modern machines, no matter how simple or complex they are, still depend on the same four principles. The moving parts of every machine are simply combinations of the wheel and axle, the lever, the screw, and the wedge, put together in many different ways to do many different kinds of work.

THE WHEEL AND AXLE

The wheel is the simplest and by far the greatest of all man's inventions. In the thousands and thousands of years that man has lived on earth there has never been an invention to equal it in importance. The wheel and axle, the straight shaft through the center of the wheel on which it rotates, are a single unit. One is useless without the other, and they work together as one device to run our present-day world.

All transportation, including airplanes and steamships, is dependent on wheels. So is every machine and, indeed, every man-made article that moves or has moving parts. Without the wheel we would still be living in caves or mud huts like men of prehistoric times.

Nobody knows who invented the wheel, but the credit for its invention belongs wholly to man. There are no wheels in nature, and no living creature was ever born with wheels. Yet somehow, long before the dawn of history, the ingenious brain of man discovered the principle of the wheel. We can only guess how it happened.

It is not unlikely that thirty or forty thousand years ago when primitive man roamed the forests of the world in search of food, one particular man, tired of carrying the heavy carcass of a wild beast on his back, sat down on some fallen logs to rest. Perhaps the logs on which he had dropped the dead animal began to roll. And perhaps this primitive man realized for the first time that rolling

dead animals or other heavy loads on logs would save him the great effort of carrying them. Probably it was many centuries before the first wheel developed from the basic idea of rolling. And it must have been many more centuries before the wheel became the first crude wheel and axle.

When we think of wheels, most of us immediately visualize a vehicle—a bicycle, an automobile, or a locomotive—that rolls along the ground. But wheels are also essential to rotary motion, the constant movement which is the basis for all engines and motors. Any vehicle will roll along the ground on its four wheels if given a push, just as a toy car does. But it cannot start by itself and keep moving unless it is pulled by an animal or run by a motor. The engine or motor we use to keep our vehicles moving contains many rotating wheels attached to a shaft and a gear wheel which transmits power to the wheels of the vehicle. Without rotary motion, the movement of a wheel going around and around, we would not have engines to power our machines.

The wheel and axle has hundreds of other applications that are equally important in

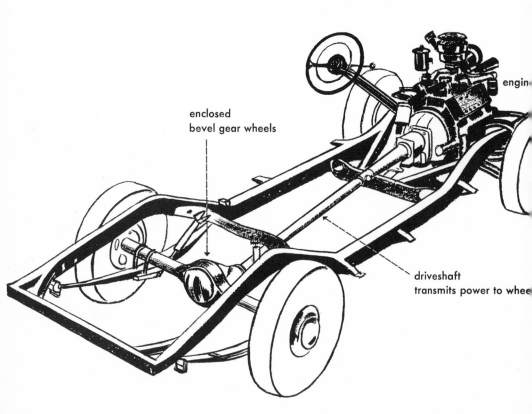

engin

enclosed
bevel gear wheels

driveshaft
transmits power to whee

modern life. Most of the machine tools, kitchen utensils, household goods, furniture, toys, and other articles that we use every day are made on machines called lathes. Sometimes there are as many as a hundred lathes in a factory, each one belted to a single set of overhead wheels which rotate on a common axle. The overhead wheels run all the lathes at the same speed, and in this way it is possible to produce a hundred identical articles in the same amount of time that it takes to produce one. In other words, wheels make mass production possible.

All wheels give us rotary motion of some kind, but there are many different kinds of wheels which do special kinds of work. The gear wheel, which makes it possible to regulate the action of one wheel in relation to another, is one of the most important of these special types of wheels.

The rim of a gear wheel, instead of being even and smooth like the rim of a bicycle or

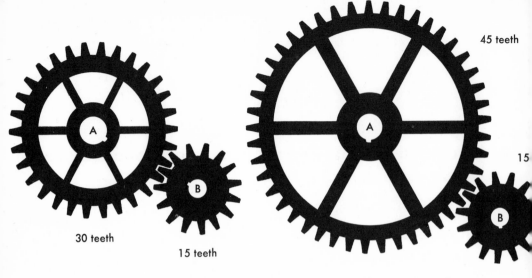

automobile wheel, is notched. These notches, called teeth, are all even in size and evenly spaced around the wheel. When the teeth of two gear wheels are fitted together and one wheel is turned, the projecting teeth of the turning wheel force the second wheel to turn in the opposite direction.

Now here is the important fact: if wheel A has twice as many teeth as wheel B, wheel B will turn twice as fast as wheel A when the two wheels are brought together and turned. If wheel A has three times as many teeth as wheel B, wheel B will turn three times as fast as wheel A when the two wheels are brought

[26]

together and turned. By varying the number of teeth in the gear wheels we can make one wheel turn as quickly or as slowly as we please in relation to the other wheel.

Your bicycle runs by means of two gear wheels. The big wheel with the pedals attached to it is a gear wheel. The hub of the rear wheel is also a gear wheel, connected to the pedal wheel by a chain. If the big wheel with the pedals on it has 50 teeth, and the small rear wheel has only 10 teeth, then for every complete turn of the pedals the rear wheel will move forward five times. Every time the pedals make one complete turn you and your bicycle move ahead five turns of the rear wheel.

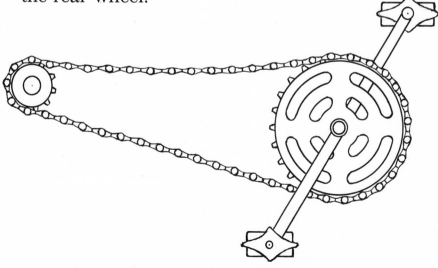

The movements of the minute and hour hands of a clock or watch are also controlled by a series of gear wheels. In a twelve-hour period, the minute hand on the face of every clock and watch moves around the dial 12 times while the hour hand moves around the dial only once; the minute hand travels 12 times as fast as the hour hand. Suppose the gear wheel controlling the minute hand has 8 teeth. And suppose the hour hand is attached to another gear wheel with 96 teeth (12 times as many as the gear wheel of the minute hand). When the two wheels are turned together by means of a strong spring, the minute hand will turn just 12 times as fast as the hour hand.

Just as the hour hand moves ¹⁄12 as fast as the minute hand, so the minute-hand wheel coming in contact with a third wheel can be made to move ¹⁄12 as fast as that wheel. And the third wheel, coming in contact with a fourth and fifth wheel, can slow down the

minute hand still further until it can be made to turn only once (a revolution) in an hour. Because of this system of gear wheels, all run by a mainspring, the two hands of a clock can keep perfect time.

Gear wheels or combinations of gear wheels are good illustrations of the rule that a little force acting over a long distance can produce great force over a short distance. By using a system of gear wheels it is possible to lift great weights with very little effort. Heavy loads of coal are lifted and dumped

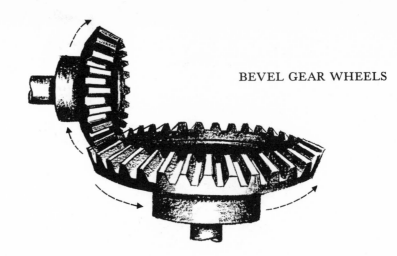

off coal trucks by a simple system of gear wheels. Today, the gears are operated automatically, but years ago the coal man did it by hand. By using a crank to turn the gear wheels and taking a long time to do it, he was able to lift many tons of coal high enough to dump it.

There are many other types of gear wheels. Bevel gears are used to change the direction of motion. This gear is especially important in automobiles, for it changes the direction of motion from an up-and-down movement to a right-and-left movement.

The cam is almost as important as the different kinds of gear wheels. The axle in this kind of wheel is usually not in the center of the wheel, so it has a lopsided motion when it is turned. As a result, a bar resting on the rim of this wheel will move up and down, up and down, in a regular or irregular motion, as the wheel rotates. This kind of motion is called cam action. It is very important in all kinds of machinery because it makes it possible to lift and drop something in a constant movement.

Tripper cams are wheels with regular or irregular projections on the rim which con-

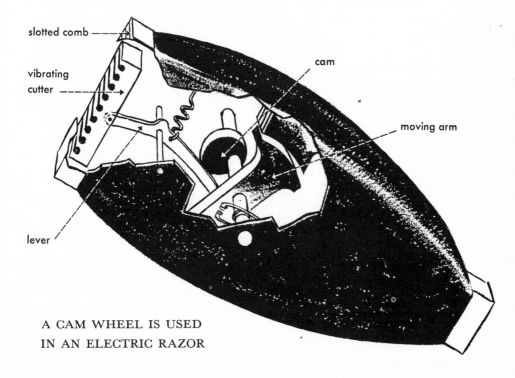

A CAM WHEEL IS USED
IN AN ELECTRIC RAZOR

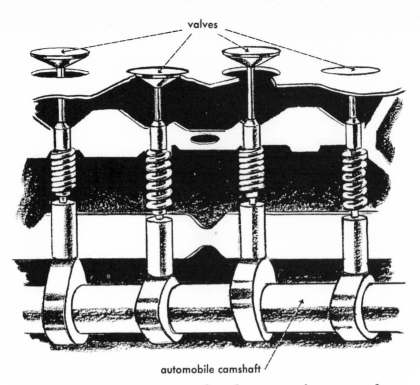

valves

automobile camshaft

trol the movements of a bar resting on the rim of the wheel. As the wheel turns, the bumps or projections on it cause the bar to rise and fall with a bang at each projection. Machines that crush salt crystals or anything else we want to make into a powder are simply cam wheels with a heavy weight attached to the bottom of the bar.

Cam action is used in hundreds of different kinds of machines, but it is only one of the hundreds of ways in which the wheel is

[32]

used. Another important use of the wheel is the pulley.

The pulley is a wheel and axle in its simplest form. Without it, it would be difficult to lift things to places out of our reach. The wheel of a single pulley has a deep groove in its rim in which a rope is run. When a weight or object is tied to one end of the rope, it is possible to lift it to the pulley by simply pulling the other end of the rope. It is this simple device that enables us to raise a flag to the top of a flagpole every morning without having to climb up the pole ourselves.

You can lift twice as much weight with two pulleys rigged together as you can with one. In this case, the upper pulley must be fixed and the lower one must be left free to move up and down the rope. But the rope will move through the lower one only half as fast as the rope moves in the upper pulley. So, although you can lift twice the weight with

two pulleys as you can with one, you can lift it only half as fast. By using many pulleys, you can lift great weights with very little physical effort. But by the law of machines, the more pulleys you use, the more slowly the weight will be lifted.

The wheel is the greatest invention of man, but it is of little use if it doesn't turn. That is why the crank, which in its simplest form is nothing more than a handle near the rim of a wheel, is so important. As you turn the handle, you turn the wheel. Even though at first glance this may seem very obvious, it is this simple idea that is the basis of all engines everywhere. For it is the crank that transmits power to the wheel and keeps it turning.

The pedals on your bicycle are simple cranks. As you press on them, your knees go up and down, up and down. And it is this up-and-down motion, transmitted to the gear wheels by the pedals, that enables you to ride along at a great clip. The crank (the pedals

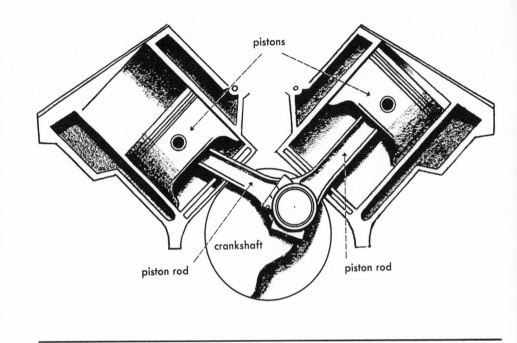

pistons

crankshaft

piston rod

piston rod

THE CRANKSHAFT OF A RAILROAD ENGINE

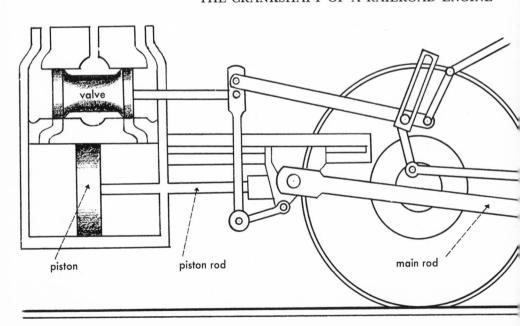

valve

piston

piston rod

main rod

of your bike) transfers the up-and-down motion of your legs into a smooth rotary motion which sends the wheel forward in a straight line.

Steam engines and gas engines work the same way. Steam pressure or gasoline explosions in an iron box or cylinder move a rod (called a piston) up and down or back and forth. This piston rod is attached to a crank on a wheel, and as the rod transmits its movement to the crank, the wheel turns. Without the piston rod and the crank, there could be no steam or gasoline engine.

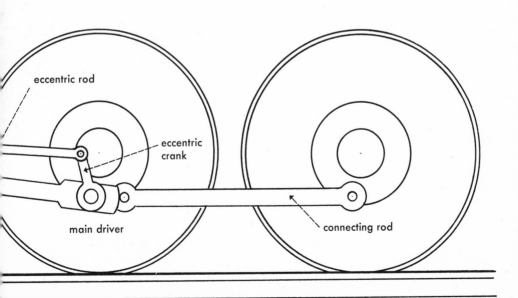

eccentric rod

eccentric crank

main driver

connecting rod

THE LEVER

The second basic principle of all machines, and by far the easiest to understand, is the lever. A simple lever is nothing more than a long bar balanced at or near its center, like a seesaw. The point on which the seesaw turns, or is balanced, is called the fulcrum; the distance from either end to the fulcrum is called the lever arm. There are many different types of levers, but they all move up and down on a fulcrum and they all have lever arms.

As you know, if two boys who weigh the same sit on the ends of a seesaw that is balanced at its center, they can move up and down just balancing each other. But suppose you weigh 70 pounds and your little sister on the other end of the seesaw only weighs 35 pounds. Naturally, you won't just balance one another. You weigh twice as much as she does, and you can keep her end of the seesaw up in the air as long as the fulcrum is midway between the two ends of the seesaw. By moving the fulcrum much nearer your end, however, and thus shortening your lever arm, her lever arm becomes long enough to lift your weight.

The reason for this is the same rule of machines we already know: A little effort over a long distance equals the same amount of work as a great effort over a short distance. The longer the lever arm—the effort arm—on one side of the fulcrum and the shorter it is on the other side—the resistance arm—the greater the weight the lever will lift with only a little effort.

A boy weighing only 100 pounds can balance a huge rock weighing 2,000 pounds and resting one foot from the fulcrum by sitting on the other end of a 21-foot lever. This is because 100 pounds times a distance of 20 feet (the effort arm) exactly equals 2,000

pounds times a distance of one foot (the resistance arm). Leverage simply means that the longer the effort arm is, the more resistance you will be able to overcome with the same effort.

The principle of the lever was also known to primitive man before the beginning of recorded history. He already knew how to use the wheel in order to move heavy weights along the ground, but he had not yet learned to use it to lift heavy weights off the ground. Then he discovered that a rock, far too heavy for even his strong muscles to lift, could be raised easily by placing it at one end of a long, strong tree branch balanced on another rock used as a fulcrum.

This was a great discovery, almost as great as the invention of the wheel, and primitive man used it without knowing or caring about the principles governing it. It was not until many centuries later that civilized man began to investigate the lever and apply it to very early machinery. A great Greek philosopher and scientist, Archimedes, who was one of the first men to explain the principles of machines, once said, "Give me a lever long enough and a place to stand and I will move the Earth." The lever is also used to change the direction of motion as well as to overcome great resistance. This is particularly true in industry.

Today, you can find levers wherever you look. In typing this manuscript on my typewriter I used many different levers. The printing presses that printed this book are a mass of levers. Whenever you pry open the cover of a pop bottle you are using a lever. Every time you use a fork or spoon to raise food to your mouth you are using a lever; your arm becomes a lever when you lift something. Whenever you cut paper with a scissors, crack a nut in a nutcracker, weigh yourself on a weighing machine, row a boat, play the piano, shovel snow, or wheel a wheelbarrow you are using a lever.

Every lever must have a fulcrum, or turning point, an effort arm where force is exerted, and a resistance arm; but the fulcrum, the effort, and the resistance may be in different positions with relation to one another. There are three major classes of levers.

In a lever of the first class the fulcrum is always between the effort and the resistance. Scissors, the seesaw, and the balance scale are good examples of this kind of lever. Here, as we already know, we can overcome great resistance by lengthening the effort arm and shortening the resistance arm.

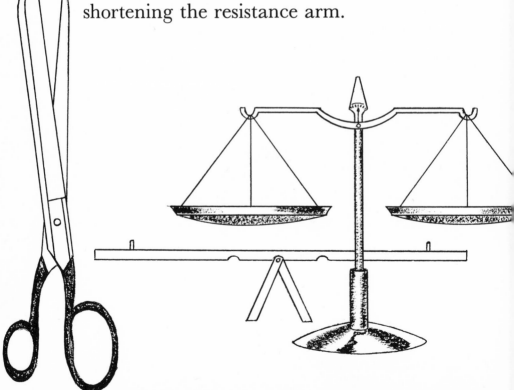

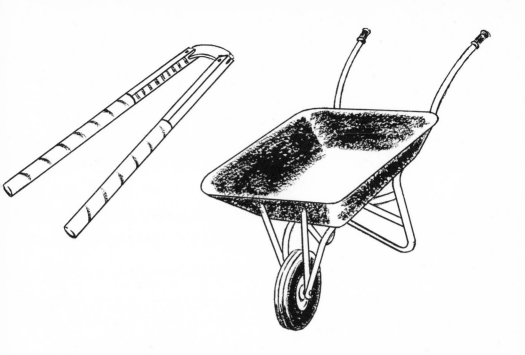

In a lever of the second class the resistance is always between the fulcrum and the effort. The nutcracker and wheelbarrow are typical examples of this kind of lever. In the nutcracker the fulcrum is at the hinge of the two arms; and the nut, which is the resistance, is between it and the effort, which is your hand. The resistance of the nut pushing up against the arms times its distance from the fulcrum must be much less than your squeezing effort times its distance from the fulcrum, or the nut won't crack. You can easily see that the longer the arms of the nutcracker, the greater will be the squeezing force on the nut. The same principle is true for the wheelbarrow. The longer the arms of a wheelbarrow, the greater the load you will be able to lift and wheel along. In this case the wheel is the fulcrum.

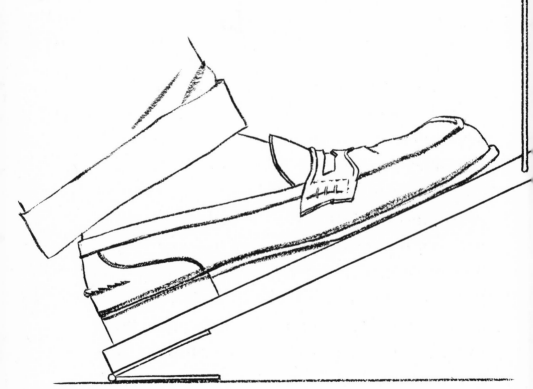

In a lever of the third class the effort is always between the fulcrum and the resistance. The shovel, forearm, and a foot pedal in a machine are common examples of this class. In the foot pedal the fulcrum is the hinge where the pedal is attached, the effort is your foot pressing on the pedal, and the resistance is the pull of the bars which are attached to the object you are moving above the pedal. In the forearm the fulcrum is at your elbow, the resistance is the weight you are lifting, and the effort is the muscle between your elbow and your hand.

Levers can be any one of these three classes or combinations of two or all of them. Compound levers like the hammers of a piano or the keys on a typewriter can become quite complicated. By a combination of various compound levers your weight can be balanced by a little piece of iron weighing less than a pound. This is what happens when you weigh yourself on the scales.

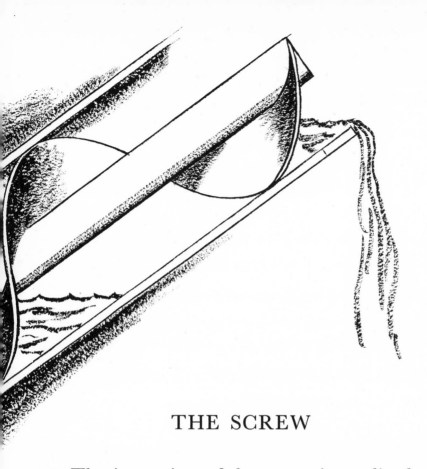

THE SCREW

The invention of the screw is credited to the Greek scientist Archimedes, who was the first to use it to raise water from the sea to the deck of a ship. The Archimedean screw was simply a spiral tube on a shaft which could be turned by hand. When the crank was turned round and round, water was lifted right up the spiral tube onto the deck.

Everyone has seen a common screw, and everyone knows that when the screw is turned with a screwdriver the threads move very slowly up or down, depending on the direction in which the screw is turned. The distance between the threads on the screw is called the pitch, and this distance is extremely small, seldom more than a quarter of an inch. This means that one complete turn, or revolution, of the screw will raise or lower it only one quarter of an inch and in most cases even less than that.

We already know from the law of machines that a little effort exerted over a long distance can lift a great weight over a short distance, and that the smaller this distance is, the greater will be the lifting force. When the distance lifted becomes as small as a quarter of an inch for each revolution, as it does in a screw, the lifting force becomes incredibly great. That is why the screw is the most important of the four basic principles of machines for producing enormous pressures and lifting very heavy weights.

A house can be lifted right off the ground in order to move from one place to another by using jackscrews to raise it. The jackscrew is a large screw with a pitch of about a quarter inch. It is turned at the top by means of a bar 5 feet long which a man inserts into one of four openings. He then pushes this bar for a quarter turn, removes it, and inserts it into the next opening and

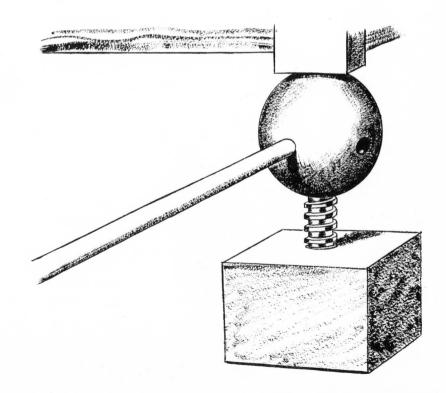

turns it another quarter turn. After doing this four times, the screw has made one complete revolution and the house is lifted a quarter of an inch. It takes a long time to lift the house a few feet, but in this way it is possible for a man using a force of only 40 pounds on the bar to lift an object weighing about 30 tons. The jackscrew is a fine example of the lever and screw working together to lift tremendous weights with little effort.

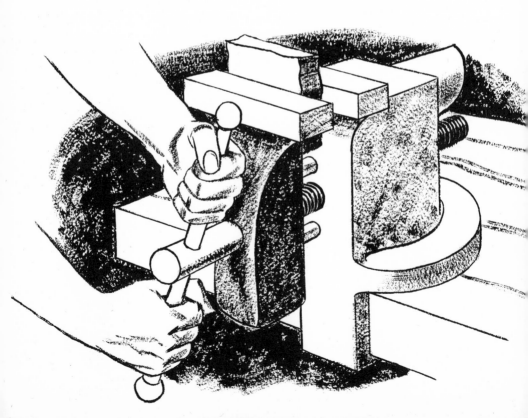

The same principle also works in reverse. By moving the screw down instead of up, you can produce a pressure of 60,000 pounds with a force of only 40 pounds.

The combination of the screw and the lever can produce great pressure, far greater than any human muscle can produce. The carpenter and mechanic's vise, which is nothing more than two plates of wood or metal on a large screw, is a simple, but important example. As you turn the lever handle the two plates come together very slowly, depending on the pitch of the screw on which they are mounted. The time you use and the distance your hand travels in turning the lever arm is changed into enormous pressure which holds the work firmly in place while it is being shaped or cut. No carpenter or mechanic could operate his shop without this simple machine.

What is true for the vise is also true for nuts and bolts, thumbscrews, and clamps of all descriptions. The screw is the strongest means known of fastening two things together. One of its most obvious but also one of its most important applications is its use in plumbing and hardware fixtures. Water taps would not turn on and off without the screw. All water pipes and, in fact, any kind of pipes which must be joined together securely are connected by threaded screws. The screw is so important in our daily lives that it would be difficult to list the hundreds of times we make use of it every day.

The screw's primary function in machinery is to exert enormous pressures and lift tremendous weights. Neither the wheel and axle nor the lever can do the same job so well. It is also used in machinery to produce a steady, slow motion. By making the pitch of the screw smaller, the motion can be made slower. It all depends on the pitch, or number of threads to the inch, on the screw.

One of the most interesting applications

of the screw is the micrometer. This little instrument measures thicknesses to $\frac{1}{1000}$ inch. It consists of a frame and a movable part that turns on a screw with 40 threads to the inch. When the screw is turned one revolution, the movable part will move $\frac{1}{40}$ inch. By moving the screw only $\frac{1}{25}$ revolution, the movable part moves only $\frac{1}{1000}$ inch, or $\frac{1}{25}$ times $\frac{1}{40}$. In this way, it is possible to measure thicknesses too small for the eye to see. No precision work can be accomplished without the use of the micrometer.

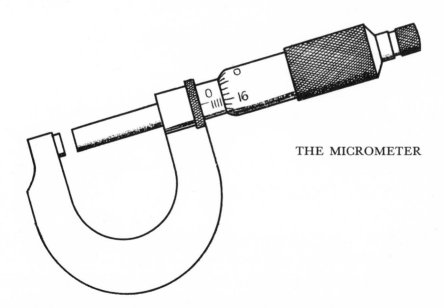

THE MICROMETER

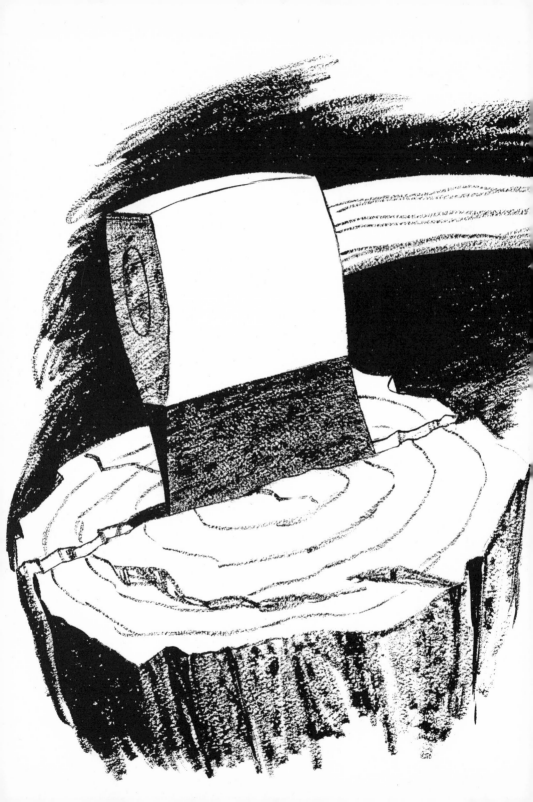

THE WEDGE

The wedge, the fourth basic principle of machines, is nothing more than a thin piece of wood or metal with sloping sides. The general rule which applies to all wedges is this: The greater the length of the wedge in relation to its thickness, the easier it is to drive it through a resisting body. Because of this the wedge is the basis of all cutting tools such as the ax, the chisel, the razor blade, and the knife.

The paper and printing industries use the wedge in their enormous presses for cutting paper. Large quantities of paper—several thousand sheets—are stacked in these presses and held firmly under pressure, which is applied by means of the screw. Then a huge sharp knife—really a wedge—is dropped with enormous force. It cuts the entire lot quickly, smoothly, and accurately in a single stroke.

Printers use the wedge in another important way. Have you ever wondered how printers make the margins of the type on a book page so even? If you have ever typed a letter, you know how hard it is to keep the right-hand margin straight. On a typewritten page it is usually uneven, but on a printed page it is always perfectly even, thanks to the wedge. Little wedge-shaped pieces of metal are forced in between the words on a line of type when it is set up on the linotype machine. Some are forced deeper than others to vary the spacing between the words, and in this way the lines of type can all be made the same length. Very few people realize that it is the wedge that makes this possible.

Every needle and every pin is also a wedge. We think of a sewing machine as a combination of wheels, screws, and levers. But without the wedge, its needle, the machine would not sew, and the modern clothing industry could not exist. This simple principle of the

wedge—a tapering piece of wood or metal—
plays a very important part in our lives.

These four basic principles of machines—
the wheel and axle, the lever, the screw, and
the wedge—can be applied to machines in
an endless variety of ways. Some machines
use only one or two of them; others use all
four principles in a series of complex actions.

The phonograph is a fairly simple machine
that uses all four principles. The arm of the
phonograph is a simple lever, and the needle
point is a form of the wedge. The turntable
is, of course, a wheel and axle. And the record
itself, with its spiral groove, is an excellent
illustration of the principle of the screw, even

though in this case it does not exert any great pressure and is not used for that purpose.

The linotype is a more complicated machine which is used for setting type for newspapers, magazines, and books. The operator of a linotype machine sits at a typewriterlike keyboard, pressing down the keys just as though he were typing a letter. Each time he presses a key the principle of the lever is applied, and a small brass mold with that letter cut in it drops into line. As we already know, the lines are spaced out to equal lengths by wedges fitted between the words. As soon as a line of type is complete, it is cast into lead by forcing the hot molten lead into the box containing the brass type molds. As soon as the lead hardens, the type, now set in one complete line, is removed. A long lever comes down, picks up the little brass molds, and places them on a cylinder with a slowly revolving screw thread at the top of the machine. As the brass molds travel slowly along

this thread from left to right, each letter is sorted automatically, released, and dropped into its proper slot, ready to be used again.

So the linotype, too, uses all four of the basic principles of the machine: first, the lever, run by a series of gear wheels (the wheel-and-axle principle) from the motor, then the

wedge for spacing between the words, and finally the screw thread on the cylinder which separates the type and drops it into the proper compartments.

There is not a machine in the world that does not make use of one or more of these basic principles. And the more complicated the machine, the more these principles are varied and combined. The next time you are in an automobile or near any other machine see whether you can distinguish for yourself the wheels, the levers, the screws, and the wedges of which it is composed.